KU-174-678

World of science

SOUND AND HEARING

BAY BOOKS LONDON & SYDNEY

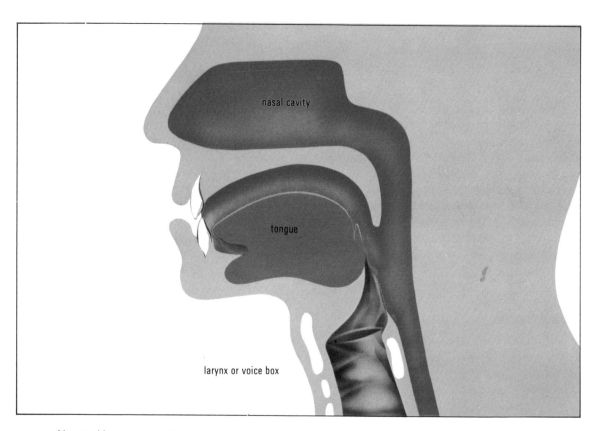

nasal cavity

tongue

larynx or voice box

Above: Human sounds are produced in the larynx – better known as the voice box

Below: The strings of the violin vibrate and produce sounds.

tongue, lips and teeth. Although babies can make sounds, they cannot speak until they learn to use their tongues, lips and teeth to shape sounds into words.

Animal sounds vary too, but not all are produced in the same way. Bees, for example, make their buzzing noise by vibrating their wings very rapidly. Some birds have two parts to their voice box and so two notes can be produced at the same time.

Musical instruments

Musical instruments produce sound in four basic ways. *Stringed instruments* have taut strings which vibrate when they are plucked, struck or played with a bow, as in a violin. The *pitch* can be changed by altering the length of the strings, either by stopping the string on a fingerboard or by having a set of strings of various lengths, as in a harp or piano. The heavier the string, the lower the note because the frequency of vibration is lower. This is why the low-note strings on a guitar or piano are heavier than the other strings.

Percussion instruments such as drums are similar to stringed instruments but they have a taut skin, or *membrane,* instead of a string. The smaller or tighter the skin the higher the note produced when it is struck. Tuned percussion instruments such as bells or the xylophone have tubes or bars that sound a note when struck. The tube or bar vibrates in a similar way to the vibrating string.

Woodwind instruments, such as the flute, have a pipe with holes closed by fingers or keys. You make the air in the pipe vibrate by blowing at the mouthpiece, which often contains a vibrating *reed* or membrane. Brass instruments work differently. You still make the air column in the instrument vibrate but several different notes can be obtained by altering the pressure of the lips on the mouthpiece. This series of notes is called the *harmonic series.* The different notes are obtained because the air column in the instrument can vibrate as a whole, as two separate halves, three separate sections and so on. In each case, the pitch of the note is raised by various amounts, making *harmonics* or overtones. Some instruments have valves

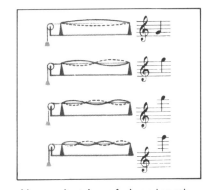

Above: A string of given length and tension vibrates in several ways at the same time. The different vibrations produce harmonics.

Below: These African musicians' drums have tautly stretched skin tops which produce musical notes when they are struck.

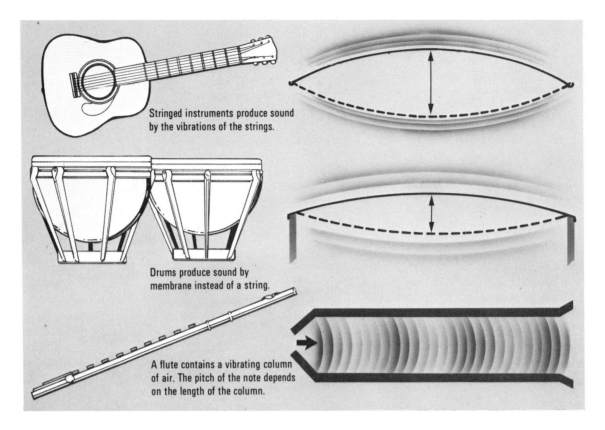

Stringed instruments produce sound by the vibrations of the strings.

Drums produce sound by membrane instead of a string.

A flute contains a vibrating column of air. The pitch of the note depends on the length of the column.

Different musical instruments all use vibration but they produce different kinds of sounds.

which open sections of tubing while others, such as the trombone, have a slide you can move to obtain other notes between the harmonics.

Almost all musical sounds contain the basic notes and harmonics, although most harmonics are not loud enough to be easily distinguished, except in deep bell sounds. The main effect of harmonics is to give a sound the quality that lets us distinguish between the same note played on different instruments.

Electronic music

Instruments such as synthesizers and electronic organs produce their sounds completely by electronics. Oscillators produce electric signals with the same frequencies as musical notes and these go into a loudspeaker. The signals cause part of the loudspeaker to vibrate and produce musical sounds. Instruments such as the electric guitar and electric piano are half mechanical and half electronic and make an enormously varied range of sound.

Opposite: The electric organ, the synthesizer and guitar all use electronic devices to create, increase and amplify musical sounds.

electronic organ

electric guitar

synthesizer

THE EAR

The human ear (below left) is very different to those of the dog (right) and the vampire bat (below right) which are far more sensitive. Both dogs and bats have a greater hearing capacity than man. The pitch of the squeaks made by a bat is too high to be heard by the human ear, but bats' ears are so sensitively balanced that they can even pick up their echoes from ordinary solid walls

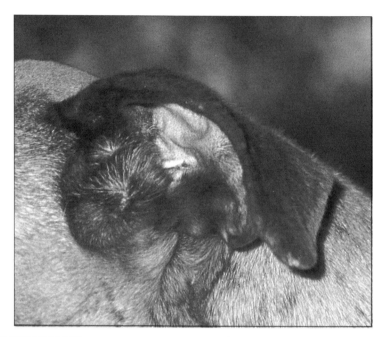

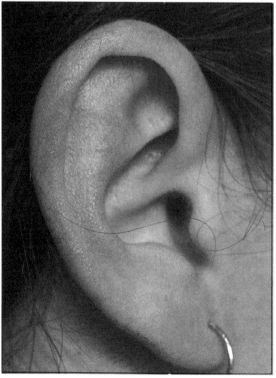

Your ears allow you to hear sounds. Usually you learn to speak by listening to your parents and imitating them. This is why children who cannot hear, either from birth or because of an illness or accident, find it so hard to learn to speak. They must learn finger signs or copy the movements of people's lips because they cannot hear the sound being made.

The fleshy flap at the side of your head, which you normally call your ear, is only part of this amazing organ. The ear has three major divisions; the *outer ear,* the *middle ear* and the *inner ear.*

The outer ear

The scientific name for the external fleshy flap is the *auricle* or *pinna.* It acts as a funnel for sound waves, leading them into the *external auditory canal,* a tube about 2.5 cm long which forms the inner part of the outer ear. The auditory canal carries the sound to the internal part of the ear.

The ear is divided into three areas: the outer, middle and inner ears. The outer ear catches the sound vibrations and funnels them through the external canal into the middle ear. These are then transmitted from the eardrum to the inner ear and changed into nerve signals to the brain.

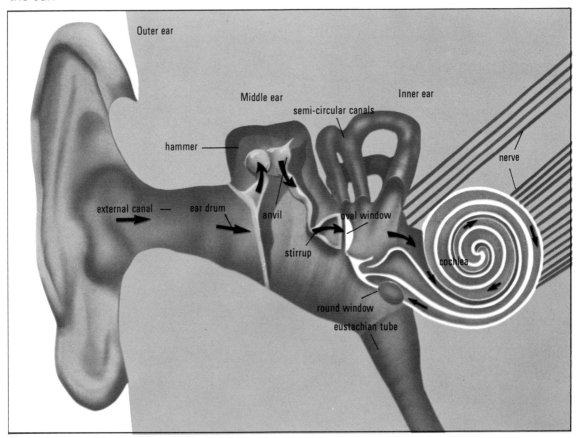

Outer ear

Middle ear

Inner ear

semi-circular canals

hammer

nerve

external canal — ear drum

anvil

oval window

stirrup

cochlea

round window

eustachian tube

The middle ear

The auditory canal ends in a membrane about 6 mm across called the *tympanic membrane* or *eardrum.* This separates the outer and middle ears and sound waves cause it to vibrate. Attached to the inner surface of the eardrum is the first of three very tiny bones – the *malleus* (hammer), *incus* (anvil) and *stapes* (stirrup). These bones are hinged together and transmit the sound vibrations across the middle ear cavity from the eardrum to another membrane called the *oval window,* which separates the middle ear from the inner ear.

If you have trouble hearing when you have a cold this is probably because a tube called the *eustachian tube,* which connects your ear with the back of your throat, becomes blocked. This means that air cannot get in and out of the middle ear. Air must be able to get in and out to balance the air pressure on both sides of the eardrum, otherwise the eardrum cannot vibrate properly in response to sound. Swallowing hard or yawning can help to open the eustachian tube and make the pressure inside your ear equal to the pressure outside, so that you are able to hear clearly again.

The inner ear

When the sound waves reach the oval window, they are transmitted to the *cochlea,* a part of the inner ear which turns them into the nerve signals which are sent to the brain. The whole of the inner ear is made up of a complicated series of tubes called the *labyrinth.* This part of the ear senses when you are about to lose your balance and the result is that you move to regain it.

The cochlea looks rather like a snail's shell, made up of a spiral of about $2\frac{1}{2}$ turns. Although tiny, it is very complicated inside and like the rest of the inner ear is filled with a watery fluid called *endolymph.* Along the length of the cochlea's spiral is a thin structure called the *basilar membrane.* Attached to this is the organ of Corti, which produces the signals sent to your brain along a nerve called the *auditory nerve.*

High-pitched sounds cause the strongest vibration near the base of the cochlea, close to the oval window. Low-pitched or bass notes, on the other hand, cause the strongest vibration near the top of the cochlea. This allows your brain to distinguish sounds of different pitch depending on which part of the organ of Corti vibrates.

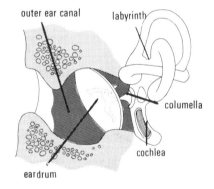

outer ear canal   labyrinth

columella

cochlea

eardrum

Unlike the human ear, a bird's ear has no pinna. The eardrum of the bird is larger than man's, and the middle ear shorter. Also there is only one ear bone, the columella, instead of three.

SOUND WAVES

Sound travels through air and other substances in the form of sound waves. When you speak, vibrations of the vocal chords in your voice box or larynx vibrate and cause sound waves. When these waves strike your ears, they cause your eardrums to vibrate and you hear a sound.

Making sound waves

A sound wave is produced when any object vibrates rapidly in the air. This object may be the string of a guitar, the vocal chords in the throat, the cone of a loudspeaker or a fallen cup shattering as it hits the floor. As one surface of the vibrating object moves forward, it pushes into the air around it and compresses the air. The air is first compressed at the surface of the vibrating object and this region, called a *compression,* starts to move away from the surface. As this happens, the surface moves backward, creating a region of low pressure, called a *rarefaction.* As the surface vibrates to and fro, a series of these compressions and rarefactions is set up in the air and these make up sound waves.

Below: The height of the crest or trough is called the amplitude. The wavelength is the distance between these crests or troughs.

Bottom: When a tuning fork is vibrated, sound waves are produced as a result of alternating higher and lower pressure at the point of the vibration.

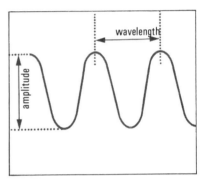

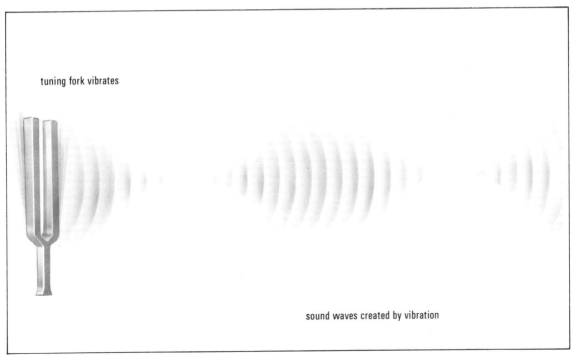

tuning fork vibrates

sound waves created by vibration

Wavelength, frequency and pitch

In a sound wave, the distance between one compression and the next or one rarefaction and the next is called a *wavelength*. The number of compressions or rarefactions that are produced in one second is called the *frequency* of the sound. Frequency and wavelength are related to the *pitch* of sound, that is, how high or low it sounds. The greater the frequency, the shorter the wavelength and the higher the pitch. For example the musical note middle C has a frequency of 256 vibrations per second and the C an octave (eight notes) higher has twice this frequency, 512 vibrations per second. Frequency is usually expressed in hertz (written as Hz). One hertz is equal to one vibration (or cycle) per second. Most human beings can hear a frequency range of from 20 Hz to about 20,000 Hz.

Because greater frequency results in higher pitch, the pitch changes as the frequency changes. On some musical instruments such as the trumpet, altering the pressure of the lips changes the frequency of the vibrations. On other instruments, such as a violin or flute, a string or key is pressed down to alter the wavelength and produce higher or lower pitched sound.

The pitch of a sound is related both to frequency and wavelength. The drum, which makes a low pitched sound, has a low frequency and, therefore, a longer wavelength than a whistle which has a high pitched sound.

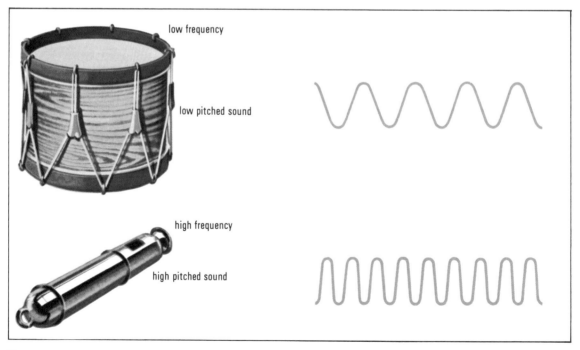

low frequency

low pitched sound

high frequency

high pitched sound

Amplitude and intensity

The harder a guitar string is plucked or the harder a trumpet is blown the louder will be the sound produced. This happens because the vibrating surface moves a greater distance as it vibrates to and fro and so produces stronger compressions in the sound waves. The sound is given more energy this way and the vibrations are said to have greater amplitude. The extra energy does not make the vibrations any faster, for this would raise the frequency; instead it makes them more powerful and so the sound produced is louder. The sound *intensity* describes the amount of energy the sound has and sound intensities are often compared using units called *decibels*.

A pistol shot has a greater intensity (amount of energy) than a cork being pulled out of a bottle and makes a louder sound.

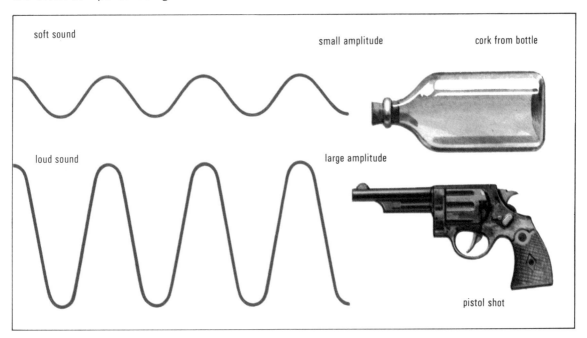

soft sound

small amplitude

cork from bottle

loud sound

large amplitude

pistol shot

Loudness

The greater the intensity, the louder the sound, but sounds with the same intensity may have different frequencies and will not sound equally loud. Very high and very low notes sound quieter than middle range notes, although they may have the same intensity. So loudness measurements are related to a sound of a given frequency. To measure loudness we use a unit called a *phon.*

The speed of sound

Below: Sound travels more slowly than light. Thus, when a cannonball is fired, the observer sees the gunsmoke before he actually hears the shot itself.

Bottom: A sonic boom is created when an aeroplane exceeds the speed of sound, because, at that speed, the air particles cannot move aside out of the way of the aircraft. This creates shock waves which are heard on the ground as an explosion.

Sound travels through the air rapidly, though still much more slowly than light. When you talk to another person, you do not notice any time lag. But if you watch a game of cricket at a large ground, you will notice that the sound of the ball striking the bat is heard slightly after you see a hit take place. This is because the sound takes noticeably longer than light to travel the distance from the players to the spectators. Sound travels at 1,224 kilometres per hour (760 miles per hour) in air at a temperature of 0°C. This is about one kilometre in three seconds or one mile in five seconds.

Cannon shot

The sonic boom

below the speed of sound

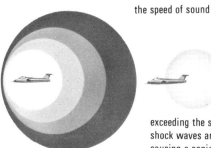

the speed of sound

exceeding the speed of sound, shock waves are created, causing a sonic boom

When an aircraft reaches a speed faster than the speed of sound, that is more than 1,224 km/h, we say it has broken the *sound barrier.* Supersonic aircraft such as the Anglo-French Concorde are designed to fly much faster than the speed of sound, but this can create problems with *sonic boom.* Pressure changes are transmitted through the air at the same speed as the speed of sound. If the aircraft flies below this speed, the air particles react to the pressure changes above and below the plane's wings and move aside to let the aircraft pass. But if the aircraft exceeds the speed of sound, the air particles do not move aside and shock waves are created above and below the wings. This thrusting aside of the air causes an explosion, or blastwave, that is felt on the ground. This sonic boom can break windows and damage the roofs of houses.

Sound travels about four times faster through water than through air and through steel it travels about fifteen times faster.

The Anglo-French Concorde is a supersonic passenger aircraft and, although it has reduced air travelling times considerably, many environmentalists object to the sonic boom which it makes.

This 1877 Edison phonograph was the first sound recording machine. It consisted of a tinfoil covered cylinder and a hand crank. He later modified this machine to produce a new motor-driven cylinder version of this player.

There are three main ways to record sound. *Disc* recording is used to produce records for record players. *Magnetic* recording is used to put music or other sounds onto magnetic tapes or cassettes and *optical* recording is used for the sound track of films.

The development of sound recording

The earliest sound recording was made by Thomas Edison in 1877. The Edison system used cylinders, first of tinfoil, then of wax. In 1887, Emile Berliner introduced recording on rotating grooved discs. Early recording systems were called acoustic or mechanical recordings. In the 1920s electronic recording replaced the acoustic method.

Stereophonic sound recording was introduced in the 1950s to give more realism to recorded music. Systems with four separate sound tracks appeared in the early 1970s and were called *quadraphonic.*

How sound is recorded

For all systems of sound recording, the sound is collected by microphones. If more than one microphone is used, the electrical signals from them must be balanced before they are mixed together. Because the volume of sound in a concert hall is very great, an electronic compressor is used to reduce the volume to one suitable for recording and playing back on your record player. From the compressor, the signals pass to a control system which adjusts their overall strength to a level suitable for recording. The signals are then fed through a power amplifier which operates the recording system.

When you speak into a telephone microphone, the sound waves are received by a vibrating diaphragm. They are changed into electrical signals which are then transmitted along wires to the earpiece speaker device which receives the sounds.

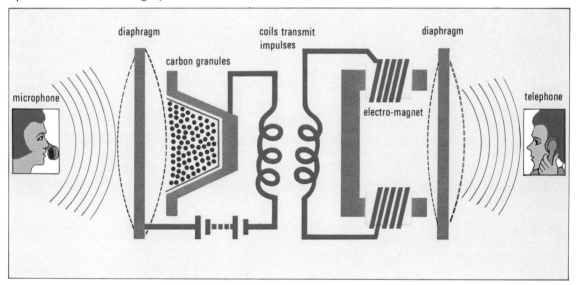

Making discs

In disc recording, a pointed chisel-shaped piece of sapphire is used. This cuts a spiral groove in the rotating lacquered surface of an aluminium disc. The sapphire vibrates in time with the sound signal and this causes corresponding variations in the groove being cut.

The lacquered disc is called the *original.* It is electro-plated and the plating is then backed with a metal support and removed from the original. This new disc called a *master* is actually a negative, that is, the *ridges* correspond to the *grooves* that were in the original. It is used to produce a *mother* which has grooves like the

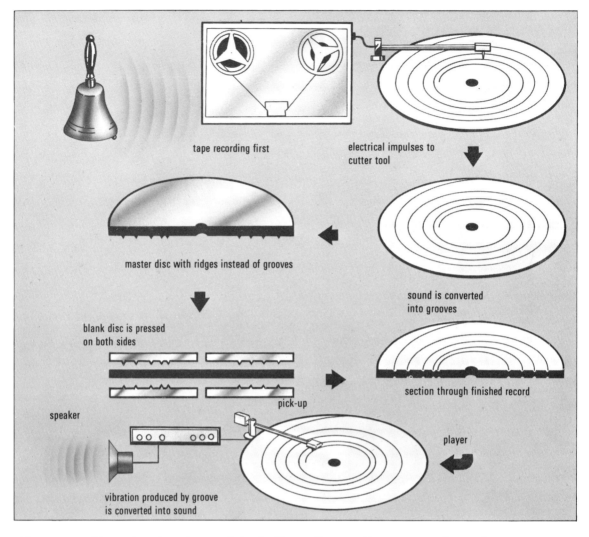

tape recording first

electrical impulses to cutter tool

master disc with ridges instead of grooves

sound is converted into grooves

blank disc is pressed on both sides

pick-up

section through finished record

speaker

player

vibration produced by groove is converted into sound

How a record is made: when the master tape is played, the cutting tool vibrates in time with the sound signal. As it does so, it cuts a pattern of grooves on a rotating lacquered aluminium disc. These grooves are an exact copy of the sound vibration.

original. From the mother, a number of *stampers* are made. To make a record, a disc of vinyl is placed between two stampers which have been heated. The plastic on each side of the disc softens in the heat and forms an impression with grooves the same as the original.

Magnetic recording

For magnetic recording on tape, the signals from the power amplifier are fed to a magnetic head and used to create a magnetic field. The tape, made of plastic, coated with crystals of iron oxide, passes through this magnetic field and the crystals make patterns that correspond to the original sound.

Recording on film

In *optical* recording, the sound is recorded on the same piece of film as the pictures, but alongside them. The signals from the power amplifier are fed to a device which causes variations in the width or brightness of the strip of film, called the sound track. When the film is projected, a light beam shines through this strip onto a photoelectric cell. This gives out electrical signals that vary according to the amount of light falling on it and these signals are fed to a loudspeaker to recreate the original sound.

In both disc and optical recording, the sounds are normally recorded on tape first and then transferred to discs or film.

The record player

This modern record player, with its circular turntable and pick-up head has a sensitive vibrating stylus which picks up the vibrations from the grooves in the disc. These are converted into electrical impulses and are then passed through an amplifier to a loudspeaker and are amplified into a copy of the original sounds.

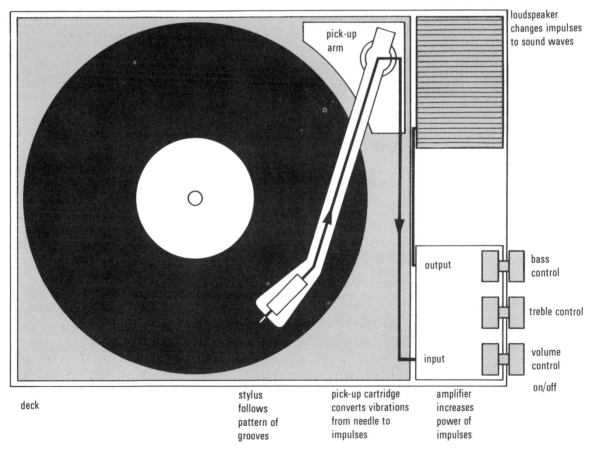

pick-up arm

loudspeaker changes impulses to sound waves

output

input

bass control

treble control

volume control

on/off

deck

stylus follows pattern of grooves

pick-up cartridge converts vibrations from needle to impulses

amplifier increases power of impulses

Record players used to be called gramophones or phonographs. Today, because many have a *stereophonic* or two-track speaker system, they are often called 'stereos', or 'hi-fi', high-fidelity, sets. The first phonograph was invented by Thomas Edison in 1877. It was crude and the quality of the sound was very poor, but speech and music could be recorded and reproduced.

Modern record players consist of a circular turntable, a pick-up head with a sensitive needle, an amplifier, controls and one or more loudspeakers. The turntable can be rotated by an electric motor at one of several fixed speeds. These are usually 78, 45 or $33\frac{1}{3}$ revolutions per minute (r.p.m.). The motor must rotate the disc at the exact speed that the original lacquer disc rotated. The pick-up consists of a lightly suspended arm containing the pick-up head with its needle, or *stylus,* usually with a sapphire or diamond tip. When the disc is rotating, the pick-up arm is lowered so that the stylus enters the start of the spiral groove.

As the disc rotates, the stylus must move in accordance with the small variations in the shape of the groove.

The signals from the vibrating needle pass to the pick-up head and then to an amplifier. These amplified signals are then passed to the loudspeaker where electrical signals reproduce the pattern of the original sound waves and we hear the music, speech or other sounds.

In a *stereophonic* system, two separate sound tracks are recorded on opposite walls of the groove and each set of signals is amplified and passed to the loudspeaker. The two sets of sounds we hear at the same time are what we know as stereophonic sound.

The stereo and quadrophonic systems give three-dimensional sound by recording through more than one microphone and amplifying through different loudspeakers. Thus we can hear two or four sets of sounds all at the very same time.

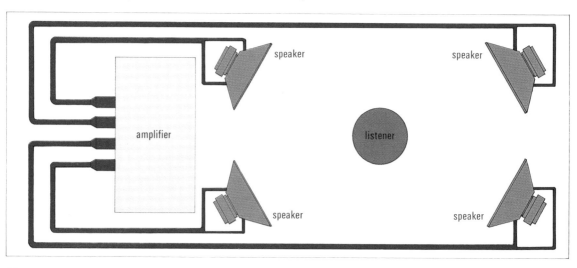

speaker

speaker

amplifier

listener

speaker

speaker

Whenever we go to a concert hall or cinema, we expect to be able to hear the music being played or the sound track of the film being shown. We expect the sound to be neither too loud nor too soft, and we expect to be able to hear it clearly no matter where we sit in the audience. The science of designing halls and cinemas so that the audience can hear properly is called *acoustics,* from a Greek word meaning 'to hear' and the people who study and use acoustics are acoustical engineers.

Concert halls

Concert halls also need to be quiet and pleasant inside, no matter how noisy it may be outside. This is done firstly by using sound-absorbent materials within the building. These materials are usually porous and soft, such as curtains, carpets, plaster and acoustic tiles. Secondly,

The Royal Festival Hall, like other modern concert halls, is designed to allow the audience to hear the music throughout the hall without confusing echoes.

noise entering a building can be reduced in these ways; by sealing any openings where sound could get in; by building thick walls; by constructing unconnected walls with dead spaces in between them.

Echoes

One of the most important aspects of sound which affects acoustics is *echo.* An echo is a sound that has been bounced off or reflected from a surface. Hard surfaces made of stone, concrete or wood reflect sound well and so produce a strong echo. Soft surfaces such as cloth absorb sound and produce little echo. In every room or auditorium, we hear two sounds, the original sound from an instrument or the speaker's mouth and the echo of this sound reflected from the walls, floor and ceiling. If the echo arrives at the ear only a small fraction of a second after the original sound, you cannot hear the echo as a separate sound. This happens if the room is small. If the room or hall is large the echo may arrive some time later and it will make the original sound hard to hear properly. This happens in cathedrals where the walls are made of stone and are a long way from the speaker. If a speaker is some distance away from you in a cathedral, often you may not be able to understand what he is saying because of the echo.

Reverberation

In some rooms or halls, a sound can be reflected more than once, so you may hear several echoes. A closely grouped series of echoes produced in this way is called *reverberation.* Each echo is much softer than the one before but if the sound goes on reverberating the original sound will be lost.

Although it may seem that the best way to deal with reverberation is to build a hall using sound-absorbing materials so that the surfaces produce no echo at all, the sound then has a dull, lifeless quality. So some echo is actually good to have. Acoustical engineers have found that the best possible *reverberation time,* the time after which the echoes have died away, is from 1 to $2\frac{1}{2}$ seconds, and rooms used for speech need a little less echo than halls used for music. You can get a rough idea of the amount of echo and reverberation in a room simply by clapping your hands sharply together once and listen-

This modern concert hall has been designed specifically for its good acoustic properties. The sound is reflected throughout the hall so that it can be heard clearly wherever one is seated.

ing carefully for the echoes.

Another problem in acoustics is making sure the sound is loud enough at the back of the hall. It may be made stronger simply by using amplifiers, although these do not always reproduce the original sound perfectly.

The pitch or frequency of sound also affects the design of halls and theatres. If the hall is not properly designed, high sounds may be absorbed more than low sounds. Sound in which high frequencies are too loud will have a thin, shrill quality, and low frequencies will have a full, muffled quality.

Acoustical engineers also have to know how sound travels through various materials. Water and hard surfaces such as metal transmit sound well, while air and soft surfaces such as window curtains do not. These qualities can affect things such as the kind of wall coverings and seats that are used in a concert hall. Human bodies also absorb some of the sound, so when a new hall is being designed, the engineers also allow for the effect the audience will have on the sound.

Acoustic tests

Two kinds of special rooms are used to test the acoustic qualities of equipment. An *anechoic chamber* is a room

This Greek open-air theatre at Epidaurus was designed in 340 BC. The ancient Greeks were quick to realise that people absorb sound, thus effectively blocking sound from one another. So, with good acoustic common sense, they designed their theatres so that members of the audience did not screen each other.

This loudspeaker is being tested in a chamber where the walls are lined with sound-absorbing materials. The acoustical quality of a building governs audibility and clarity and the quality of transmitted sounds.

lined with sound-absorbing materials which produce no echoes. Loudspeakers and microphones can be tested in this chamber. The opposite is a *reverberation chamber* where all the surfaces are hard and shiny so they reflect sounds. These chambers are used to test noisy machinery.

The Sydney Opera House

When designing a hall or studio, there are many factors to consider. Engineers must test the acoustics of the hall as it is being built and tests are often made on a scale model of the hall. For example, a great many tests both with a scale model and in the building itself had to be made to design the best possible acoustics for the Sydney Opera House.

The harbour setting of the building is very beautiful, but it created special problems for the acoustical engineers. They had to overcome noises outside such as helicopters flying overhead and ocean liners blowing their sirens right outside the building. Also, the concert hall needed to carry the full range of notes from the orchestra to the back seats with as little delay and echo as possible. The engineers wanted the sound reaching the audience to be as close to the full, rich tones heard by the conductor as it could be.

One of the devices used in the concert hall is a series of clear perspex 'doughnut' shapes called *acoustic clouds*, which hang from the ceiling and can be raised or lowered. They quickly reflect the music back down to the orchestra so that they have their own little acoustic system which they can hear without affecting the sound that the audience hears.

The Sydney Opera House is one of the triumphs of modern architecture. The acoustic system is so good that the audience sitting at the back of the concert hall can clearly hear the full tones of the music.

Radio waves

Radio uses invisible electromagnetic waves to send speech, music and other signals from one place to another. These waves travel at the speed of light, almost 300,000 kilometres per second. The waves can pass through air, space and some solids. To use radio, the sender of the information must have a radio transmitter, that is, equipment which produces radio waves and can make the waves carry speech, music and other signals. At the other end, there must be someone with a radio receiver which can pick up the radio waves and turn them back into the original signals.

When someone is transmitting radio waves of speech, music or other sounds we say they are *broadcasting*, that is, they are *casting* the waves into the air over a *broad* area so that large numbers of people can pick them up on their own radios.

Radio waves were first demonstrated in the late 1880s by a German scientist, Heinrich Hertz who found that radio waves could be produced by sparks of electricity. He also found these waves could pass through the air and cause electric current to flow in a loop of wire several feet away. Many people took part in the early development of radio. One of the most famous was an Italian, Guglielmo Marconi, who saw that radio would have an important future in long-distance communication.

The vacuum tube

The early methods of producing and receiving radio waves were very crude. Modern radio began to develop in 1907 when Lee de Forest developed his *triode vacuum tube.* This vacuum tube was important because it could be used as an *oscillator,* the part of a radio transmitter which produces an electric signal that can be transmitted through the air as radio waves. The vacuum tube replaced the old, clumsy method of producing radio waves by electric sparks. Soon, transmitters were more powerful and more reliable. By 1912, contact could be made by radio between San Francisco and Hawaii. By 1914, many ships had been equipped with transmitting and receiving devices. Radio communication was useful in both World Wars, and the period 1914-1945 saw great advances in radio.

Opposite: Inside the Sydney Opera House. Notice the acoustic 'clouds' hanging from the ceiling – these are used to reflect the music back to the orchestra.

Above: Marconi was a pioneer of modern radio. In 1896 he patented the first radio.

As vacuum tubes were very big, and bulky, so radio receivers were very large. In recent times, tiny devices called transistors have been developed. These take up much less space, so radio receivers can be made smaller than a box of matches, while radio transmitters can be hidden in a cuff link.

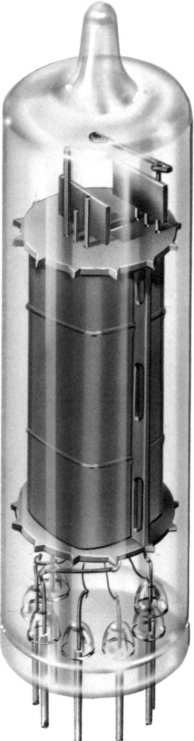

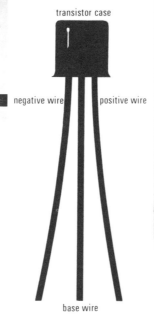

transistor case

negative wire   positive wire

base wire

Opposite: This announcer is relaying his programme from a studio in a radio station.
Top left: Transistors helped to miniaturise electrical circuits
Top right: This radio transmitter is so small that it can be cleverly concealed in a cuff link. Above: Modern technology is now so advanced than this radio receiver is even smaller than an ordinary box of matches. Far right: Radio receivers were once enclosed in bulky vacuum tubes — far larger than the miniature transistor.

The radio transmitter

A radio transmitter consists of a number of sections or stages, each with a special job. The first stage, the *oscillator*, creates an electrical current which reverses or changes direction many thousands or millions of times every second. It is also of very high frequency. The frequency of the radio waves which the transmitter produces depends on the frequency of the alternating currents produced by the oscillator.

The second stage is the *modulator*, which changes or modulates the alternating currents produced by the oscillator so that they carry an electrical copy of speech, music or other signals. It combines the alternating current from the oscillator and the electrical speech or music signals coming from a record, tape recorder or microphone.

The third stage, known as the *amplification* stage, receives the modulated currents and amplifies them to increase their power. The amplified currents from this stage are then fed into the antenna of the transmitter. The

Two types of aerial: The high accuracy glass fibre dish aerial (below left) and the sophisticated Radio Australia repeater station aerial (below right). An aerial has identical transmitting and receiving properties and may be used simultaneously for both of these functions.

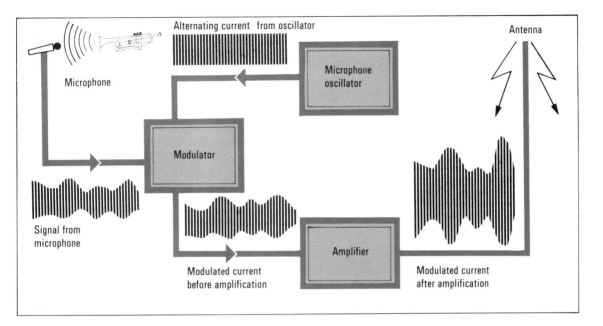

Alternating current from oscillator

Microphone

Microphone oscillator

Antenna

Modulator

Signal from microphone

Modulated current before amplification

Amplifier

Modulated current after amplification

antenna allows the energy of the alternating currents to leave the transmitter and be radiated as radio waves. With directional antennae, the radio waves are radiated mainly in one direction. Other types of antennae radiate approximately equally in all directions like the ripples on water when you drop a stone into a pool.

All the parts of the radio transmitter are interrelated and have specific functions to perform. The radio transmitter changes sound into energy waves. These radio waves are then transmitted out through the air.

The radio receiver

When radio waves leave the antenna of a transmitter, they spread out, becoming weaker and weaker as they get further away from the transmitter. To receive these waves hundreds or even thousands of miles away from the transmitter, you need a receiving antenna, that is, a length of wire through which the radio waves produce very weak alternating currents. Because the receiver antenna is designed to pick up signals of different frequencies from different transmitters at the same time, we also need a device which can *tune in*, or select radio signals coming from a particular transmitter, such as when you want to listen to your favourite radio station.

The device to do this consists of a circuit which allows the signals from a chosen frequency to be increased in power, while signals from other frequencies are rejected. Having selected the required frequency, the signals are then fed into the first vacuum tube or transistor stage of the receiver.

Right: This policeman is using a pocket-sized 'walkie-talkie' radio set to talk to someone.

Below: This radio receiver receives radio waves at its aerial and amplifies these signals. They pass through a loudspeaker and are converted into sounds.

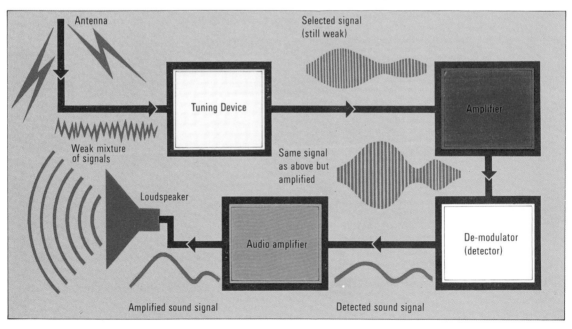

Antenna

Selected signal (still weak)

Tuning Device

Amplifier

Weak mixture of signals

Same signal as above but amplified

Loudspeaker

Audio amplifier

De-modulator (detector)

Amplified sound signal

Detected sound signal

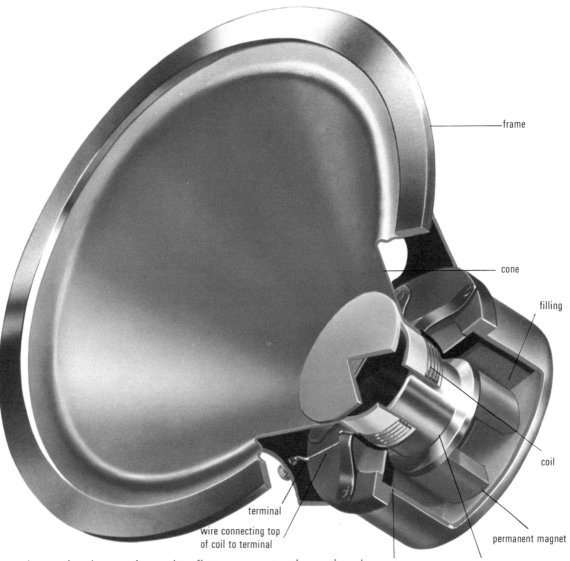

frame

cone

filling

coil

permanent magnet

terminal

wire connecting top
of coil to terminal

outer pole piece   centre pole piece

In a simple receiver, the first stage receives signals from the tuning device and amplifies them. The amplified signals then pass to the second stage of the receiver. This is known as the *demodulating* or *detecting* stage. The purpose of this stage is to receive the amplified signals and to extract from them the electrical copy of the speech or music which they carry. The signals go through a circuit which passes on pulses or short bursts of current which vary in amplitude or strength according to the original speech or music. The pulses are then smoothed out to form the sound signal.

The next stage of the receiver is called the *amplifier.* It strengthens the electrical copy of the speech or music so that it has enough power to operate a loudspeaker.

The loudspeaker changes electrical impulses into sound waves by passing them through a central coil within a permanent magnet. The magnetic field which is produced by these impulses interacts with the permanent magnetic field. The resulting magnetic force causes the coil to move and thus the cone vibrates, and then sound waves are produced.

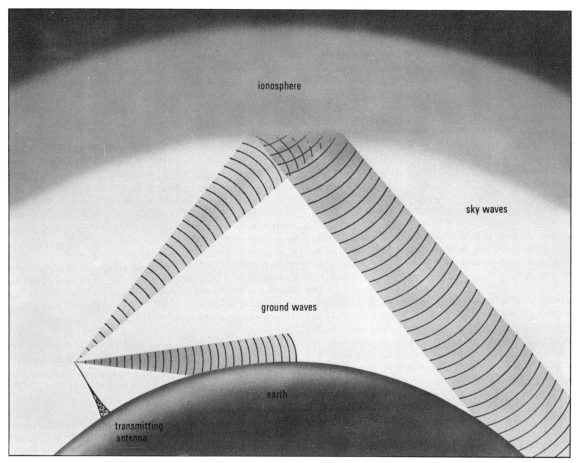

ionosphere

sky waves

ground waves

earth

transmitting
antenna

As the radio waves leave the transmitting antenna, they spread out, gradually growing weaker. Ground waves follow the earth's surface while sky waves are reflected back to the earth by the ionosphere.

How radio waves travel

After leaving the transmitter, radio waves spread through the air and space in several ways. Waves having low frequencies travel in two main ways. Some of these follow the surface of the earth and are called ground waves. Others travel through the atmosphere until they are reflected by the layer of electrically charged particles called the *ionosphere*, which surrounds the earth, far above its surface. Waves which do this are called sky waves, and they can carry transmissions over great distances. Waves with very high frequencies such as 100 million Hz are not normally reflected by the ionosphere and the strength of the ground waves weakens rapidly with distance. So the only waves that we can really use are those that travel through the troposphere, the lowest part of the earth's atmosphere. These waves are called space waves.

Radio telescopes

Radio astronomy is the study of radio waves produced naturally in various parts of the universe. These signals are produced in the gas clouds of galaxies, by planets and by some stars, including our sun. Radio telescopes are used to detect radio waves coming from space. By tuning into these waves, scientists have discovered the shape of our galaxy and worked out temperatures, distances and surface conditions on other planets.

These radio telescopes receive energy waves from distant stars and planets out in space.

Radio control

This is a means of controlling machines or equipment from a distance by using radio. It is used in space exploration and for guiding missiles and unmanned aeroplanes called *drones*, which may be used by the armed forces for target practice.

Model aircraft and boats can also be controlled by radio. The model has a small radio receiver inside. The operator, who is some distance away, works a transmitter which sends radio signals to the receiver. When the signal is received, an electric current is produced inside the receiver. This current is used to operate one of the controls of the model, perhaps the accelerator or the rudder.

The radio waves can be used to carry as many as ten different instructions to the controls of the model so that it can perform as many different actions.

Radar

Radar stands for *radio detection and ranging*. It is a way of finding the position of objects by radio waves, and it is really quite simple. Bats use a kind of radar to fly at night without bumping into obstacles. As it flies, the bat lets out a series of short squeaks so high-pitched that most human ears cannot hear them. When there is an object in the way, the squeaks are reflected back as an echo. The bat's ears hear the echo and it is able to avoid the object.

Radar works in a similar way by sending out short pulses or bursts of radio waves and catching the echoes when they bounce back. The time it takes for the echo to come back depends on how far away the object is. So, by timing the echo, you can work out how far away the object is, or its 'range'. You can see the echo as a 'blip' or bright spot on the radar screen. The screen is marked with scales to show distance and direction.

Radar is a very useful navigational aid in the air and at sea, especially at night or in bad weather. Radio waves, unlike light waves, can penetrate clouds of fog so objects in the way of a ship or plane can still be seen on a radar screen despite fog.

Opposite: Radio can even be used to control military target aircraft like the Australian plane (above), as well as the model boat on the lake (shown below).

This radar scanning system uses reflected waves to locate unseen objects. The perforated and curved aluminium sheet shown here is a reflector.

When the oscillator is switched on, it sends a pulse of micro-wave signals to the aerial These pulses are radiated out by the aerial and reflected back by the target. The reflected signals are seen as a bright spot of light on the radar screen.

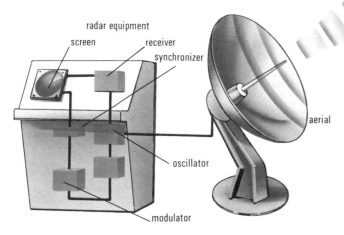

target

radar equipment

screen

receiver

synchronizer

aerial

oscillator

modulator

Below: The air traffic control tower at London airport directs the incoming and outgoing flights by using radar as a navigational aid. Thus, planes can safely land and take off even in adverse weather conditions.

THE TELEPHONE

Alexander Graham Bell

In 1876, an American, Alexander Graham Bell, patented an early type of telephone and on March 10, 1876, the first complete sentence was spoken over the telephone when Bell said to his assistant 'Mr Watson, come here, I want you'. Sound waves from the voice set up vibrations in a diaphragm which made an attached rod of magnetic material move towards and away from an electromagnet. These movements created currents in a coil which were electrical patterns of the sounds of the words. The listener's end also had a coil through which current flowed, causing another diaphragm to vibrate at that end and reproduce the original speech. However, Bell's telephone transmitted such weak currents that it could only be used over short distances. Many improvements had to be made before it could be used over longer distances.

Alexander Graham Bell (above) invented the telephone (below) in 1876. The telephone changes sounds into electrical signals which are then transmitted along wires to a receiver device.

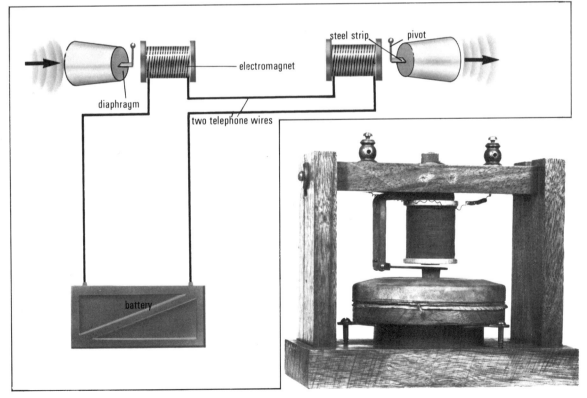

Telephone circuits

In Bell's original telephone, each end of a single transmission wire was buried in the ground so that the electrical circuit was actually completed in the earth between the two ends of the telephone wire. Then the two-wire or 'metallic circuit' was introduced, which had the effect of reducing noise and interference heard on the single-line system. So successful were the improvements that a telephone line was opened between Boston and New York, USA, in 1885.

The use of the telephone spread quickly, but soon there were huge numbers of wires strung overhead. Then these groups of wires were bound into a single cable which could be passed either overhead or through underground channels. A cable in the 1890s might have carried fifty pairs of wires. Today, this is more likely to be over 2,000 pairs of wires. Later improvements helped to reduce the total number of wires needed to carry large numbers of calls. By 1918, many more improvements had enabled large numbers of conversations to be held on a single pair of wires at one time.

Right: This technician is wiring up the control panel in a modern telephone exchange.

Opposite: Telephones are now widespread throughout the world. This Papua New Guinean, in his traditional costume, is using a public telephone.

Modern telephones

Modern telephones are essentially the same as the earlier ones, although many developments have helped make their use easier and more efficient. Most connections between one telephone user and another are now made in automatic telephone exchanges and users of the telephone can even call numbers in other countries without the need for a telephone operator. Picturephones or videophones which let the callers see each other are also being developed.

By means of radio, telephone calls can be made to places not linked by any cable, such as ships in mid-ocean. Radio telephones are also widely used between aeroplanes and ground control stations and between motor cars.

Radio telephones can now be fitted on motorcycles and cars. They are widely used by the police and ambulance services as well as fire brigades and taxis.

INDEX

HEARING AND MAKING
  SOUNDS 1-5
THE EAR 6-8
SOUND WAVES 9-13
RECORDING SOUND 14-18
ACOUSTICS 19-24
RADIO WAVES 25-36
THE TELEPHONE 37-40

Page numbers in italics refer to a diagram on that page.
Bold type refers to a heading or sub-heading.

A

Acoustic clouds 23, *25*
Acoustics **19**, *20, 21, 22,* 19-24
  tests **21**
Aeroplane *12,* 13
  supersonic 13, *13*
  unmanned 33, *34*
Amplifier 15, *17,* 21, 28, 31
Amplitude *9,* **11,** *11*
Anechoic chamber 21, *22*
Animal sound 2
Antenna 28-29, *30, 32*
Auditory canal 7, 8
Auditory nerve 8
Auricle 7

B

Balance 8
Basilar membrane 8
Bats 1, 35
Bees 2
Bell, Alexander Graham
  37, *37,* 38
Bells 3
Berliner, Emile 14
Birds 2
  ear *8*
Brass instruments 3

C

Cathedrals 20
Cochlea 8
Columella *8*
Compression (air) 9, 10, 11
Compressor, electronic 15
Concert halls **19,** *19, 20*
  design **19,** 19-24
Concorde 13, *13*

D

Decibels 1, 11
Demodulating stage 31
Discs 15-16, *16*
  master 15, *16*
  mother 15
  original 15
  recording **15**
  stampers 16
Drones 33
Drums 3, *4, 10*
  African *3*

E

Ear *1,* **6,** *6, 7,* 6-8
  bird *8*
  bones 8
  dog *6*
  human *1, 6*
  inner 7, *7,* **8**
  middle 7, *7,* **8**
  outer 7, **7,** *7*
  vampire bat *6*
Eardrum 7, 8, *8,* 9
  bird *8*
Echoes **20,** 22, 35
Edison, Thomas 14
  phonograph *14,* 18
Electric guitar 4, *5*
Electricity 25
Electric organ 4, *5*
Electric piano 4
Electromagnetic waves 25
Electronic music **4**
Endolymph 8
Eustachian tube 8
External auditory canal 7

F

Flute 3, *4,* 10
Forest, Lee de 25
Frequency 1, **1,** **10,** 11
Frequency of vibration 2

G

Greek theatre (Epidaurus) *21*
Ground waves (radio) 32
Guitar 2, 11
  electric 4, *5*

H

Harmonics 3, *3,* 4
Harmonic series 3
Harp 2
Hearing 1, 10
Hertz 10
Hertz, Heinrich 25

I

Incus (anvil) *8*
Inner ear 7, *7,* **8**
Intensity 1, **11,** *11*
Ionosphere 32, *32*

O

Opera House, Sydney **22,** 23,
  23, 25
Organ of Corti 8
Oscillator 25, 28
Outer ear **7, 7**
Oval window 8

P

Percussion instruments 3
Piano 2
  electric 4
Picturephone 40
Pinna 7
Pitch 1, 2, **10,** *10*
Phon 11
Phonograph 14, *14*

R

Radar **35,** *35, 36*
  navigation 35, *36*
  screen 35, *36*
Radio 25, 25-36
  aerial 28, *28, 30*
  broadcasting 25, *26*
  communication 25
  control 33, *34,* 33-35, *36*
  frequency 28
  method of travel **32,** *32*
  receiver 25, 27, *27,* **29,** *30,*
    29-33
  telephone 40, *40*
  telescope **33,** *33*
  transistors 27, *27,* 29
  transmitters 25, 27, *27,* **28,** 29,
    29, 33
  waves **25,** 25-36
Radio astronomy 33, *33*
Radio Australia 28
Rarefaction 9, 10
Recording disc **15,** *16*
Recording sound **14,** *16,* 14-18
  acoustic 14
  electronic 15
  magnetic **16**
  optical **17**
  quadraphonic 14, *18*
  stereophonic 14, *18*
Record player **17,** *17,* 18
  hi-fi 18
  quadraphonic 18, *18*
  stereophonic 18, *18*
Reverberation **20,** 21
  chamber 22

time   20
Royal Festival Hall   *19*

S

Sky waves (radio)   32
Sonic boom   **12**, *12*, 13
Sound
   absorbing materials   21, 22, *22*
   animal   2
   barrier   13
   high-pitched   *1, 8, 10,* 21
   human   2, *2*
   low-pitched   *10,* 21
   making   **9**
   quality   4
   recording   **14,** 14-18
   speed   **12,** *12,* 12-13
   track   17
   waves   1, *1,* **9,** *9*
Space waves (radio)   32
Speed of sound   **12,** *12,* 12-13
Stapes (stirrup)   8
Stringed instruments   2, 3, *4*
Stylus (needle)   18
Sydney Opera House   **22,** 23,
   23, 25
Synthesizer   4, *5*

T

Teeth   2
Telephone   *15,* **37,** *37, 39,* 37-40
   cable   38
   circuits   **38**
   exchange   *38,* 40
   radio   40, *40*
Tongue   2
Transistors   27, *27,* 29
Trombone   4
Troposphere   32
Trumpet   10-11
Tuning fork   *9*
Turntable   18
Tympanic membrane   8

V

Vacuum tube   **25,** 27, *27*
   triode   25
Valves   2-3
Vibration   1-3
   air column   3, *4*
   reed   3
   strings   2, 3, *3*
Videophones   40
Violin   2, *2,* 10
Vocal chords   1, 9
Voice box   1-2, *2,* 9
   bird   2

W

Walkie-talkie radio   *30*
Wavelength   *9,* **10**
Whistle   *10*
Woodwind instruments   3
Words   1-2

X

Xylophone   3